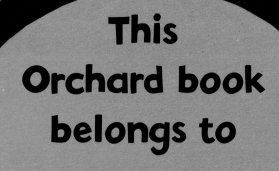

This
Orchard book
belongs to

_____

_____

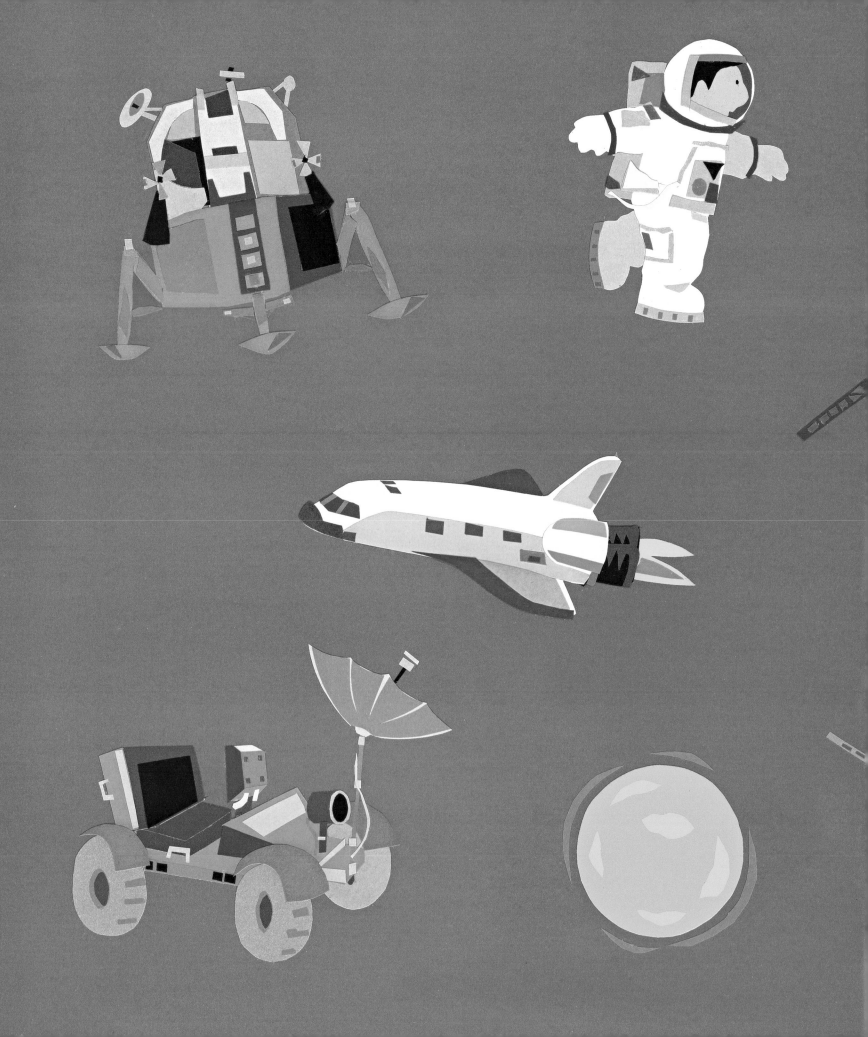

For Beth, Iain, Norman and Sheila
MM

For Tom and Harrison
AA

ORCHARD BOOKS

First published in Great Britain in 2011 by Orchard Books
This edition first published in 2016 by The Watts Publishing Group
3 5 7 9 10 8 6 4 2

ISBN 978 1 40834 931 1 • Printed and bound in China

Orchard Books
An imprint of Hachette Children's Group
Part of The Watts Publishing Group Limited
Carmelite House, 50 Victoria Embankment
London EC4Y 0DZ
An Hachette UK Company
www.hachette.co.uk
www.hachettechildrens.co.uk

Zoom, Rocket, Zoom!

Margaret Mayo & Alex Ayliffe

ORCHARD

Mighty rockets

are good at zoom, **zoom**, **zooming,**

5 4 **3 2 1** and . . .

LIFT OFF! Launching!

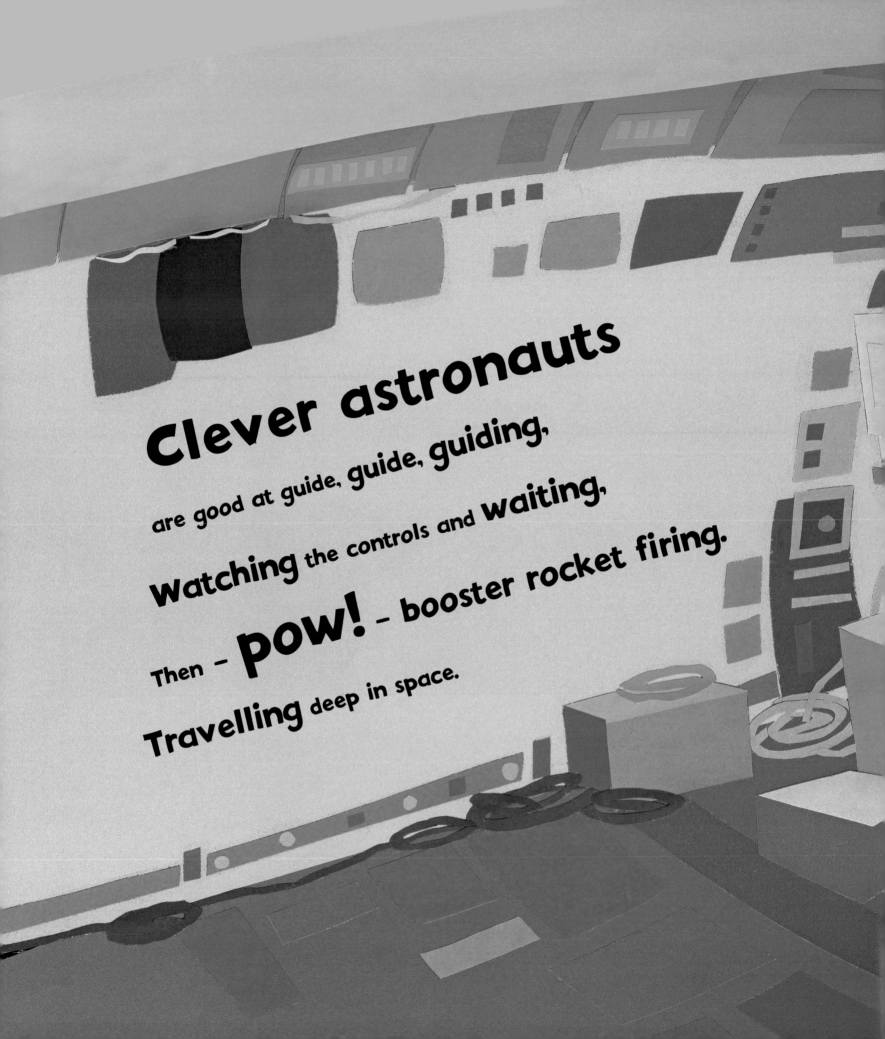

Clever astronauts
are good at guide, guide, guiding,
Watching the controls and **waiting,**
Then – **pow!** – **booster rocket firing.**
Travelling deep in space.

Lunar modules

are good at **tricky moon** landings.

They leave the spaceship, swooping, descending,

Spidery legs ready for – **Bam!** – safe landing.
Touching down in space.

Excited astronauts are good at moon walking.

Bouncing, bounding . . . Oops! No falling,

As they SCOOP up moon rocks, carefully collecting.
They can WORK in space.

Moon buggies are good at roll, roll, rolling,
Round wheels turning, soft dust gripping,
Across the humpy, lumpy moon . . . bumpety-bumping.
Driving up in space.

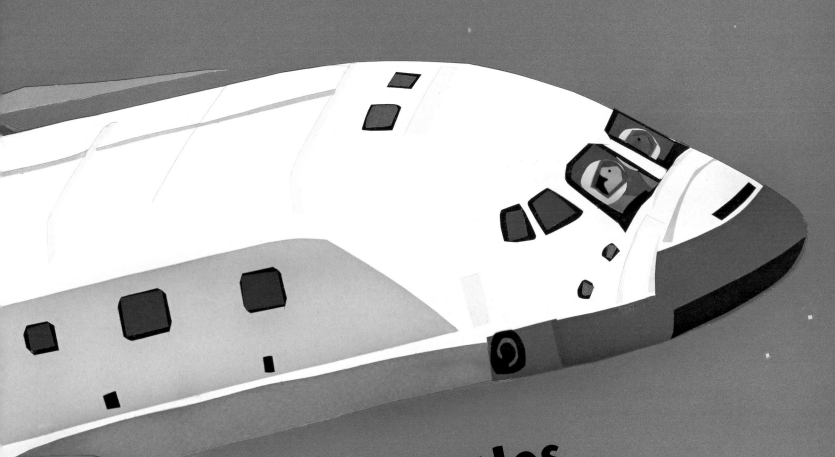

Space shuttles
are good at **big** loads **moving.**

They **hurtle** upwards, **booming, thundering,**

Off to a **space station** for fast unloading.

Carrying tools through space.

Space stations

are good places for living,

Somewhere for eating, working and sleeping,

And – **whoopee!** – weightless

somersaulting.

A **home** while up in space.

Bold astronauts are good at space walking.
They have fun . . .
arms waving . . . slowly moving . . . almost dancing,

And they can work,
building and **repairing**.
Floating up in space.

Space satellites

are good at **round-the-earth orbiting,**

Taking pictures for **weather forecasting,**

Signals receiving and – whizz! – to TVs beaming.
Circling up in space.

Robot spacecraft

are good at speed, **speed, speeding,**

Powered by the **sun,** they keep on **flying,**

Reaching distant planets and even landing.

Moving fast through space.

Robot rovers

are **good** at roam, **roam**, **roaming.**

They **trundle** over Mars, **searching, measuring,**

Red deserts **finding** and mountains **discovering.**

Exploring deep in space.

When the **night** has **come** and the **moon** shines bright,

Reflecting down to **earth** our **sun's** great **light** –

Become a **space explorer!** Watch the **stars** in the **sky!**

And look out for **satellites** . . . just **slowly gliding by!**

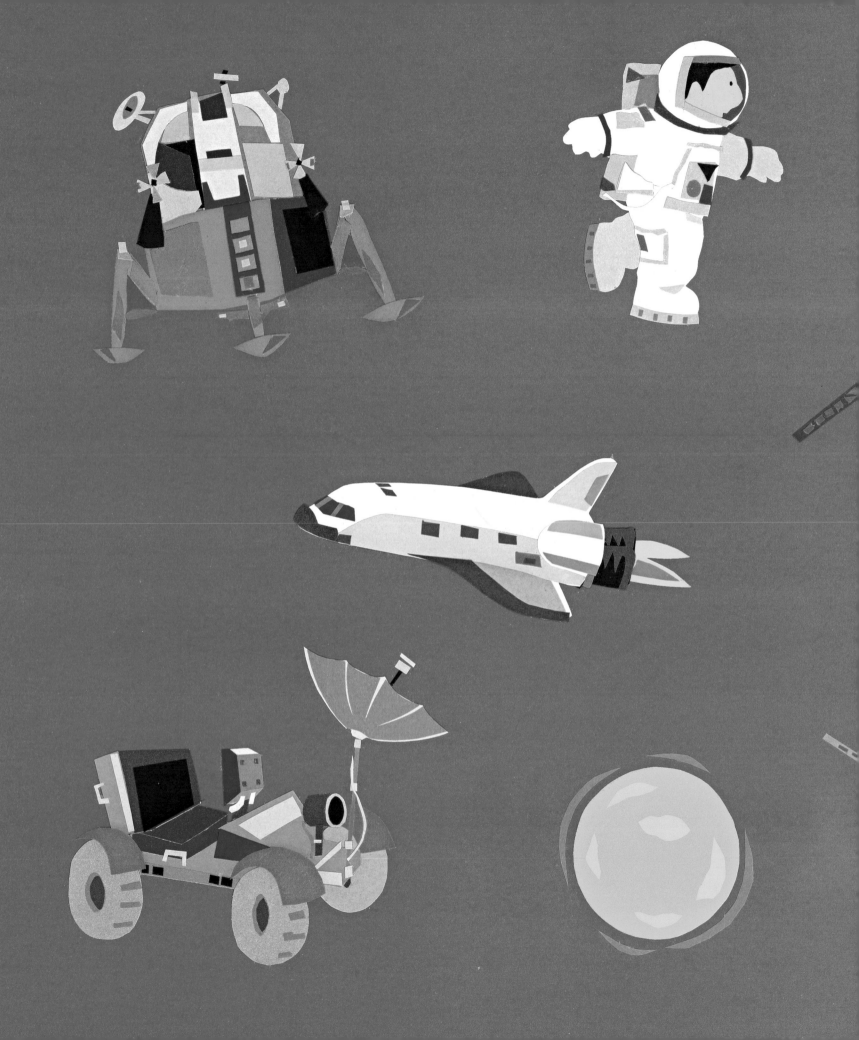